ON
EDGE

ON EDGE

BY JIM CRANE

First printing, July 1965
Second printing, August 1965

Library of Congress Catalog Card Number: 65-15933
© M. E. Bratcher 1965
Printed in the United States of America

J. 3185

JOHN KNOX PRESS   Richmond, Virginia

TO
JEANETTE

ACKNOWLEDGMENTS

Most of the cartoons in this book have previously appeared in *motive* and *The Evergreen Review*.

HAVE
YOU
TRIED
TRANQUILIZERS
?

What a lovely day
for something nice to happen.

Wonder why it never does!

It's all according to plan.

It's our world and we're stuck with it.

Come back when I'm not so busy.

Doesn't the thought of space thrill you?

I think I'm lost here.

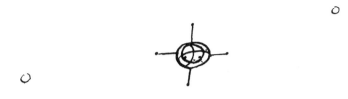

Crone

It's not so bad when the wind dies down.

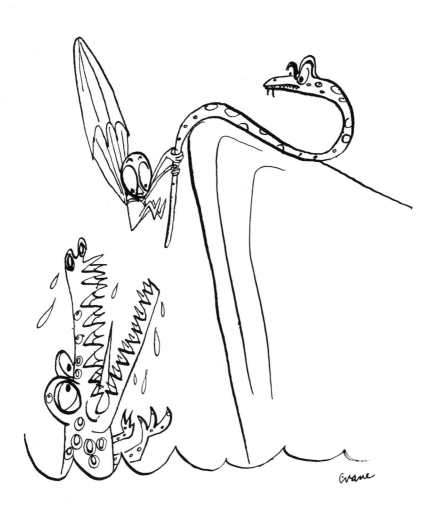

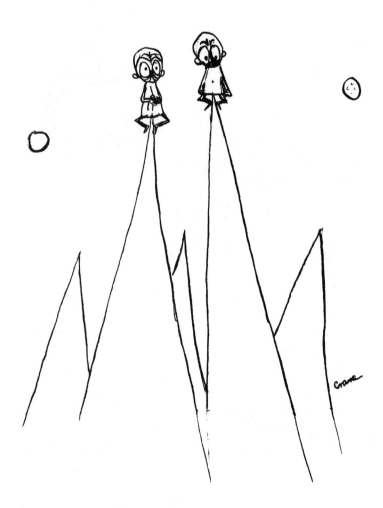

It did bother me a little when I was younger.

I'm concerned all right, but mostly about this business
Dad left me.

Have you tried tranquilizers?

100%...

In order to protect our cherished freedoms you won't mind
a few restrictions, if you're loyal.

Why aren't we happy when we've got so much?

I am genuinely sorry
for the pain of your race.

But God and man
recognize *your* suffering,

and that has meaning, you know.

. . . but who weeps for Helen Trent?

You certainly didn't expect adjusting to be easy, did you?

This century of woe and rebellion!

Our women depose us.

Our children defy us.

The communists would liquidate us.

And dark-skinned people all over the world
want to further humiliate us.

What did we adult,
white, protestant,
male businessmen ever
do to deserve such a world?

Crane

At least He is one of us.

Heh, heh, son, we got
no race problem down heah.

—Besides, why don't you
mind yoah own business?

We understand the nigra,
we got ouah traditions ta uphold.

We'd work things out in
ouah own way if it wasn't foah
outside intra fearance.

Giddy up, boy, got no time foah talkin with agetators.

I have always been a 100% American.

So I joined this society of *right*-thinking people.

Compromise!   They only wanted to go *halfway* back!

Some whites are ruthless,

scheming,

greedy,

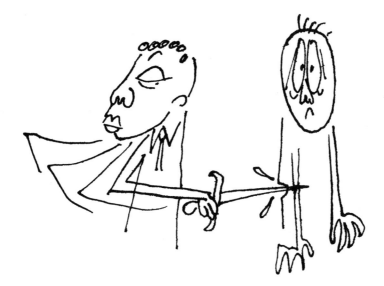

treacherous . . .

I want as miserable much for my people. What's good for
you white geese is good for us colored ganders!

First Little Rock.

Then Oxford.

We've had about enough from the South.

The Negro must be given his rights, now!   The South is his home.

And we can't have 'em up here, ruining real estate in Chicago.

Freedom

How can honorable men
cope with a ruthless enemy?

He is fanatical, diabolic, inhuman

Stern measures are necessary. Fight fire with fire!

We must learn to
think as he thinks.

Plot and scheme
as he does.

Act as he acts. Hate as he hates.

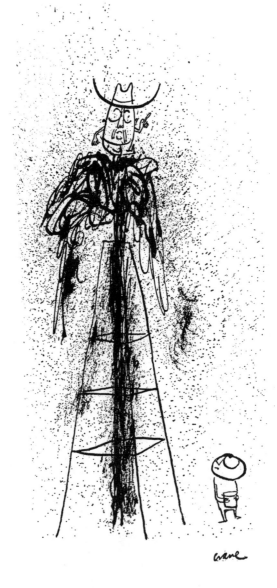

A man's gotta be self-reliant, son. Ya don' see me askin
for, nor gettin, any privileges ah don' deserve.

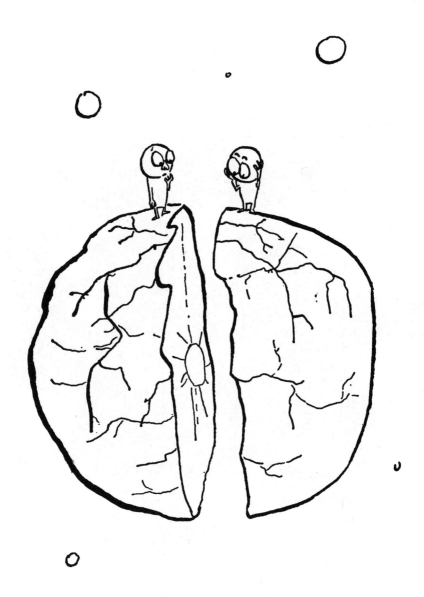

Kind of solves our problem, doesn't it?

I enjoyed your talk, Mr. Amos, but I would like to hear
more of what's *right* with Israel.

The danger is from within.

The government has become too big, too bureaucratic, too impersonal, my whole organization agrees.

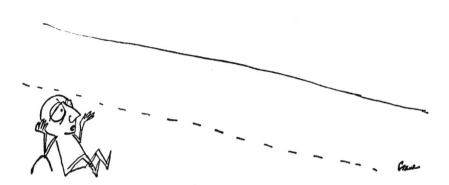

I'll meet you halfway
—from the middle.

Suppose I gave up my security and still no one loved me.

Hey, man, don't you feel the rhythm of the tension of our times?

crane

I think I love you!

If I worship you, Lord, will you give me peace of mind?

. . . and fame,
and success in business?

. . . and give a personal,
written guarantee of immortality
for me and my family?

crane

Oh—I must worship you
"because you are God"?

What kind of a deal is that?

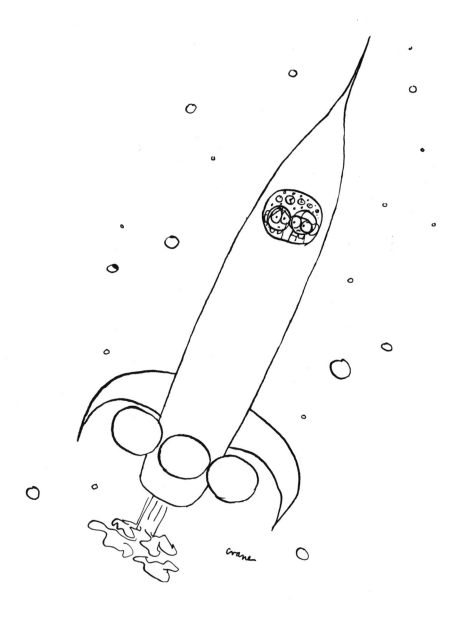

What if when we get there it isn't any better?

It's a matter of taste after all, and yours is old-fashioned.

Take us to your theologians.

Now take us to your artists.

Perhaps we'll have time to visit with your leaders next time.

Historically many improvements have been made in the cross.

Planing, sanding, oiling, gold-plating.

But now,
thanks to the miracle of technolo

and good taste, we are able to produce in luxurious foam
rubber and tufted velveteen,

a beautiful and useful item:
the decorator cross pillow.

A perfect symbol for faith in our time.

Where did it all go wrong?

Knock! Knock!

Snap!

Crane

'SPEAK
TO ME,
EVE!'

At last, national security, just for the two of us, Eve—

Speak to me, Eve!

Why should I do or be or love anything?

One bomb and all I hoped
and dreamed, up in smoke.

Suppose it doesn't happen,
though, and things just go on—

That's the sickest theory I ever heard!

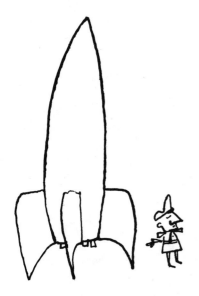

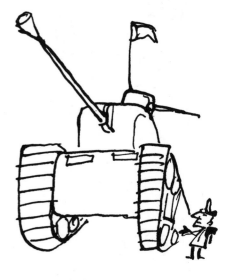

Our 1,000,000,000 ICBM's
with 100-megaton warheads

are backed up with a full arsenal
of conventional weapons

and a *third* stockpile
of clubs and stones.

Crane.

Whatever history holds
for us, we are ready.

You must admit Western civilization is dead.

Christianity has failed.

And so have reason, law, science, and philosophy.

It's time we tried something else.

O o o ops!

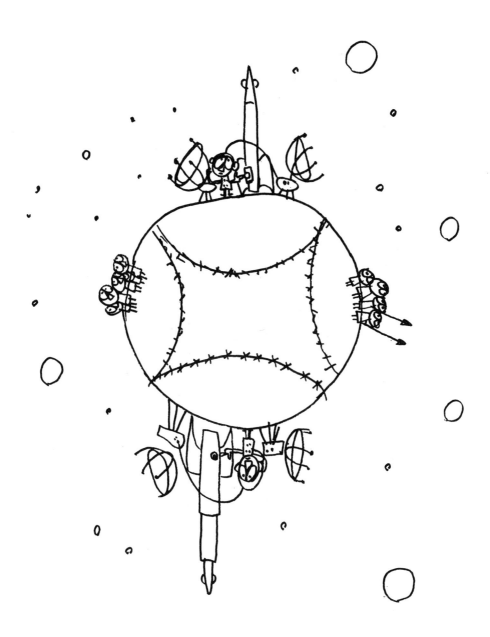

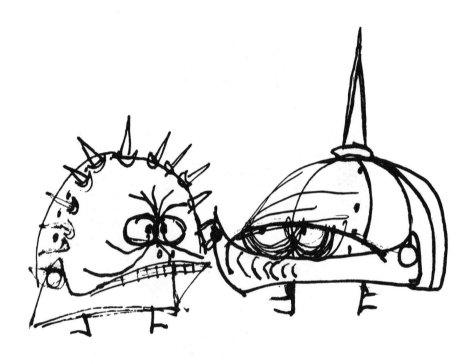

I don't know who you are, but I hate you!

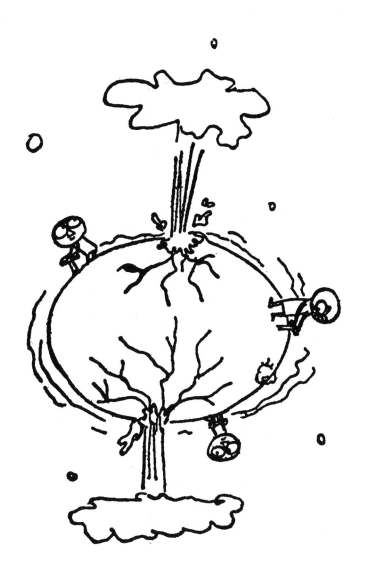

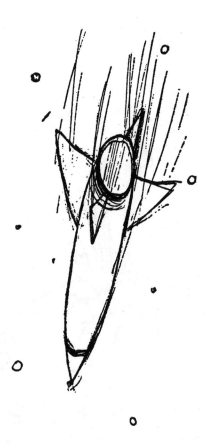

Looks like we'll have to retaliate.

You had as big a stake in testing as I did.

What is a sane position?

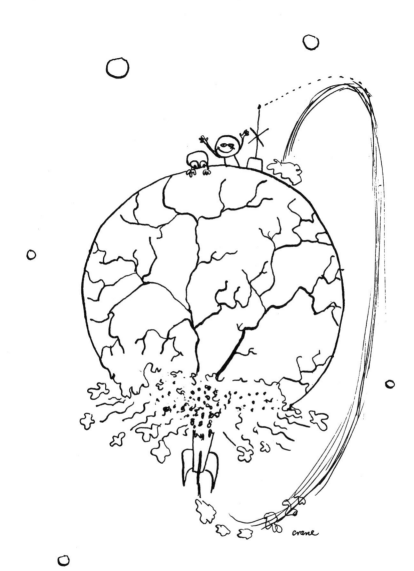

crane

Good Lord! It's a flower!